mindbending

logic
puzzles

Publisher: Simon Melhuish
Editor: Nikole Bamford
Puzzle Compilers: Lloyd King, Rich Garner
Additional Contributors: Sarah Wells, Peter Sorenti, Jane Purcell, Sue Curran
Designer: Al Shiner
Contributing Designer: Sarah Wells

Published by:
LAGOON BOOKS
PO Box 311, KT2 5QW, UK
PO Box 990915, Boston, MA 02199, USA

www.thelagoongroup.com

ISBN 978-1-906170-82-0

© LAGOON BOOKS, 2001 & 2008

Lagoon Books is a trademark of Lagoon Trading Company Limited.
All rights reserved.

Printed in China

mindbending

logic
puzzles

The Original and Best!

All New Edition!

For more fantastic puzzles go to
www.giveusaclue.com/mindbenders

INTRODUCTION

All the mindbending puzzle books have been carefully compiled to give the reader a refreshingly wide range of challenges, some requiring only a small leap of perception, others deep and detailed thought. All the books share an eye-catching and distinctive visual style that presents each problem in an appealing and intriguing way. Do not, however, be deceived; what is easy on the eye is not necessarily easy on the mind!

January
February
March
April
May
June
July
August
September
October
November
December

Aunt Tabitha was extremely touchy about her age.
When an impudent nephew was brave enough to ask her,
she cunningly replied that she was 35 years old, not
counting Saturdays or Sundays. So how old was she?

6

Three brothers entered a shop,
each needing a pair of shoes re-soled
and a key cut.
There are two assistants in
the shop, both of whom work at
the same speed.
It takes 15 minutes to re-sole
a pair of shoes and five minutes
to cut a key.
How quickly can they finish?

A man died leaving all of his money to be divided amongst his widow, four daughters and three sons. He stipulated that each daughter should receive three times as much as each son, and each son should receive twice as much as their mother. If the exact amount left was $7,936, how much should the widow receive?

R.I.P.

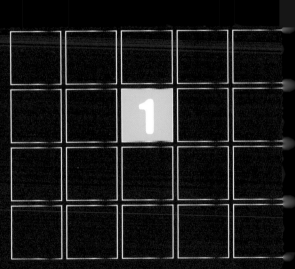

Using all the numbers 1–25, fill in the grid below so that all rows, colums and diagonals add up to 65. The first number has been placed for you.

Can you write down a straightforward subtraction sum,

a - b = c

where each of the numbers,
a, b and c is made up of all the digits 1–9 inclusive,
with each digit being used once only in each number.

A couple who celebrated their 60th wedding anniversary in 1995 were both born on August 16th, seven years apart. The man is 2,555 days older than his wife. In what years were they born?

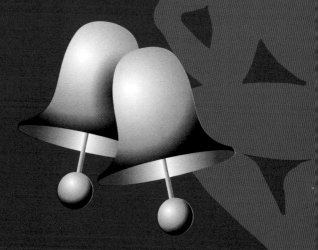

Insert plus and minus signs to achieve the results given:

12	3	4	5	6	=	10
2	**2**	**3**	**4**	**5**	**=**	**0**
7	6	2	5	1	=	7
5	**4**	**3**	**1**	**4**	**=**	**9**
8	4	5	2	1	=	8

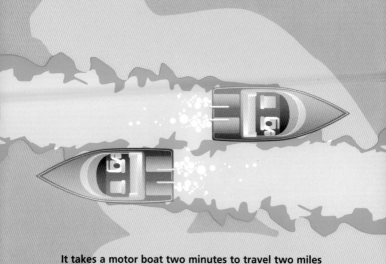

It takes a motor boat two minutes to travel two miles
when going with the current. When the boat is going
against the current it takes four minutes.
The current is always constant.
How long would it take the boat to do the same journey
in slack water when there is no current at all.

Which letter replaces the question mark?

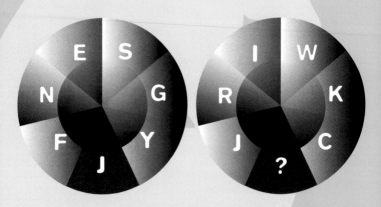

A truck driver picked up a hitch-hiker as he traveled northwards out of the city. After some time the hitcher remarked that every 10 minutes they passed a truck going in the opposite direction.

The hitcher asked the trucker 'How many trucks will arrive in the city in an hour assuming that the trucks are traveling at equal speeds in both directions?' The driver replied 'Six. It's obvious because 60 divided by 10 is 6.'

Was he correct?

If it takes a clock two seconds to strike two o'clock how long will it take to strike three o'clock?

16

BC

How old would a person born in 50 BC
be on their birthday in AD 50?

AD

If a man walks due south for four miles and then due north for three miles, what is the maximum distance he can be from where he started?

Bill and Ben's combined age is

91.

**Bill is now twice as old as Ben was
when Bill was as old as Ben is now.
How old are they?**

**What do you think should come next
in each sequence and why?**

| 4 | 6 | 26 | 666 | ? | | | |

| 22 | 20 | 10 | 8 | 4 | 2 | ? | |

| 2 | 4 | 13 | 26 | 35 | 70 | | |

| 5 1/5 | 4 1/4 | 3 1/3 | 2 1/2 | ? | | | |

| 4 | 5 | 7 | 9 | 13 | 15 | 19 | 21 |

20

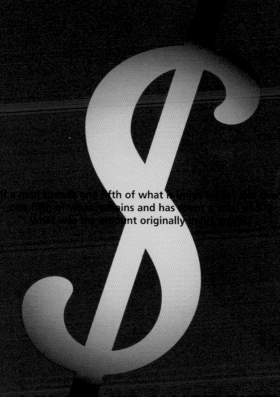

If a man spends one-fifth of what he has, saves £20, and then
one-third of what remains and has £80 left over... £
What was the amount originally in his wallet?

Divide 470 marbles between three boys so that
Andrew gets 120 more than Bill, who receives
70 more than Chris.
How many does each boy receive?

Four cards are taken and numbered 1–4. If these cards are throroughly shuffled what is the likelihood that the first four cards dealt will be dealt in order of ascendancy?

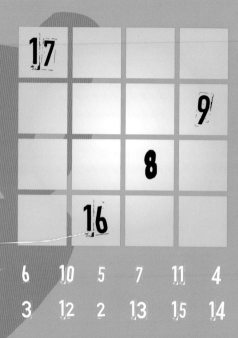

17			
			9
		8	
	16		

6   10   5   7   11   4

3   12   2   13   15   14

Put the numbers in the square so that all columns, rows and diagonals add up to 38.

24

Sally bought a bracelet for $21 which she then resold for $25. She unwisely accepted a check from the purchaser for $35 and gave him $10 change. She then gave the check to her landlord but it bounced so she had to borrow $35 to pay her rent. How much money has Sally actually lost?

Winner!!

Sam won the lottery! He spent 95 cents the first day $1.90 the next, $2.85 the next, $3.80 the next and so on. Each day he spent 95 cents more than the day before until he finally spent the last $190 of of his winnings. How much did he win in total?

If I save 1 cent on the 1st of January, 2 cents on the 2nd, 4 cents on the 3rd and double the amount every day until the last day of January then how much will I have saved by the end of the month?

Susie could not sleep. One night she went to bed
at 10.15 and read her book.
Three quarters of an hour later she put out
her light and eventually drifted off.
Sometime later a noise awoke her.
Gazing at her alarm clock she noticed that the
hands were exactly overlapping.
A little over 15 minutes later she noticed
that the digits on the radio alarm were all
the same. She dozed fitfully over the next four and
a half hours before getting up for breakfast.
What time did she get up?

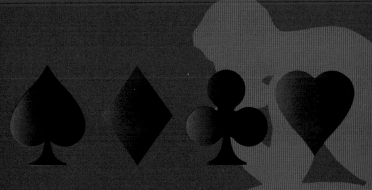

Madge, Muriel and Mandy were playing poker for fun with matchsticks. During the first round Madge won as much from Muriel as Madge had had originally. In the second hand Muriel won as much from Mandy as Muriel then had left. After the third hand Mandy won from Madge as much as Mandy then had left. At the end of the game they each had 40 matchsticks. How much did each player have at the start of the game.

What do you think should come next in each
sequence and why?

1 9 1 4 1 9 1 8 1 9 3 9 1 9 4 ?

166.66666 187.5 214.28571 250 300 ?

10 15 13 18 16 21 19 24 22 ?

940 839 738 637 ?

4 8 32 512 131072 ?

Sylvester left $650 to be divided amongst his five grandchildren, all of whom were different ages. The money was to be divided in order of age, each child receiving $25 more than the next youngest child. How much did the youngest child receive?

Hank has $200 and Frank has $96. Take money from both so that you take twice as much from Hank as from Frank and leave three times as much to Frank. How much money should you take from each?

A teapot and strainer cost $31 together.
If the teapot costs $30 more than the strainer
what is the price of each?

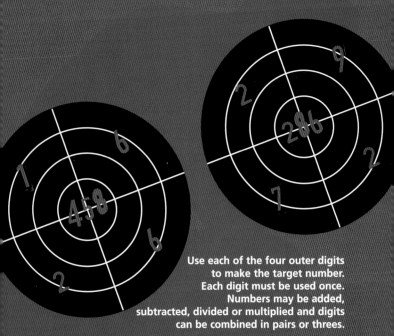

Use each of the four outer digits
to make the target number.
Each digit must be used once.
Numbers may be added,
subtracted, divided or multiplied and digits
can be combined in pairs or threes.

At any gathering there will be at least
two people who have exactly the same
number of friends present.
True or false?

A woman has three daughters who in turn each have three daughters.
If they were all together in one room:

How many pairs of sisters are there?

How many pairs of mothers and daughters are there?

How many pairs of aunts and nieces are there?

How many pairs of cousins are there?

How many pairs of grandmothers and granddaughters are there?

How many people are in the room?

Three brothers shared out 24 licorice allsorts,
each getting a number equal to what his age had been
three years previously. The youngest then proposed he
would halve his share, keep one half and divide the other
half among his two brothers. In order for him to do this
the middle brother should promise to do the same and
then the eldest. When they had done this each person was
left with eight licorice allsorts.
How old are the brothers?

Can you:

use four 4s to make 44

use five 5s to make 55

use six 6s to make 66

use seven 7s to make 77

use eight 8s to make 88

You can group the digits in pairs or threes and numbers can be added, subtracted or multiplied.

There are two clocks, one of which goes one minute per hour too slow and the other goes thirty seconds per hour too fast. If I wind them up and start them at the same time, how long would it be before one clock was exactly one hour head of the other?

A train takes two seconds
to fully enter a tunnel
which is two miles long.
If the train is traveling
at 180 miles per hour
how long will it take to
pass completely
through the tunnel?

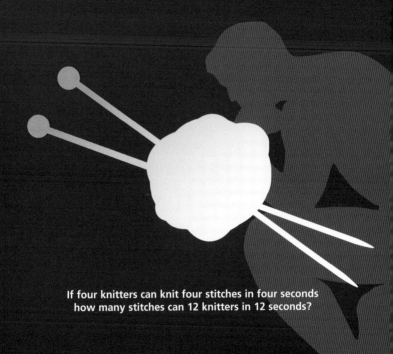

If four knitters can knit four stitches in four seconds
how many stitches can 12 knitters in 12 seconds?

When I was

14

my mother was

41

and she is now twice as old as I am.
How old am I?

Arrange

1 2 3 4 5 6 7

to form a three-digit multiple of four and a four-digit multiple of three.

Arrange

2 3 4 5 6 7 8

to form a three-digit multiple of four and a four-digit multiple of five.

Arrange

1 2 3 4 5 6 7 8 9

to form a three-digit multiple of three, a three-digit multiple of four and a three-digit multiple of five.

In a local hardware shop,
1 costs 14 cents yet it costs
28 cents for 50 and
42 cents for 144.
What is being bought?

44

A general had 28 guards with which to safeguard a
princess. He had eight lookout posts and so he arranged
his troops as below to ensure that each wall fo the castle
was guarded by nine men. (P = princess)
At the end of the first day four men were killed.
How could he rearrange the remaining men to ensure
that nine men still guard each wall?
At the end of the second day another four men are killed.
Can he still ensure that each wall is guarded by nine men?

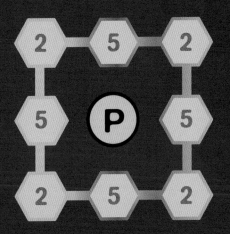

A clock manufacturer created a crazy clock where midnight is shown as 24:00. The clock struck every hour according to its 24-hour clock time so that it struck 24 times at midnight. How many times did it strike in the course of a 24-hour day?

If six squirrels can eat
six acorns in
one-tenth of an hour
how many squirrels
would it take to eat
100 acorns in
6,000 seconds?

What do the numbers 3, 7, 8, 40, 50 and 60 have in common that is not true of any other number?

How many squares are there in this diagram?

Use three identical digits
in a simple addition sum
so that the total is 12.
You cannot use the
digit 4.

If a man and a half can
tarmac a road and a half
in a day and a half,
how many roads can
six men tarmac
in seven days?

Asked about his children, a man replied,
'They are all redheads bar two, all brunettes bar two
and all blondes bar two.'
How many children did he have?

Fred dozed off during a particularly dull business presentation. He woke with a start and stole a furtive glance at his watch only to find that the hands appeared to be in exactly the same position as they had been when the meeting started. Yet the presentation appeared to be drawing to a close. What had happened?

The one-hour meeting had started between 10 and 11am. What time was it now?

Eric's mother has given him a large Christmas cake. He knows from experience that if he eats a piece a day it will take him 25 days to finish it. If he shares it with his friend, little Ernie, and they both have a piece every day it only takes 18 days to finish the cake. The sizes of the pieces of cake that Eric and little Ernie eat each day remain constant – but Eric's piece is not the same size as Ernie's. If Ernie were to eat the cake on his own, eating a piece each day, how long would it take Ernie to devour the cake.

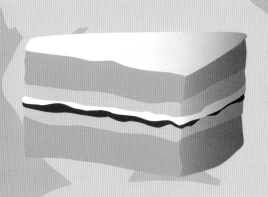

Beatrice ate two-thirds as many cakes as Annabel would
have eaten if Annabel had eaten six more than half as
many as Beatrice would have eaten if Beatrice had eaten
three less than Annabel would have eaten.
Just how many cakes did Beatrice eat?

Divide 45 pencils among four friends, Rob, Bob, Jim and Tim, so that the following is possible:
if you were to give a further two to Rob, take two away from Bob, multiply what Jim had by two and divide what Tim has by two, all four friends would end up with the same number. How many do you need to give to each person initially?

The ages of a certain father and son are the same with the digits reversed.
Nine years ago the father was twice as old as the son.
How old are they now?

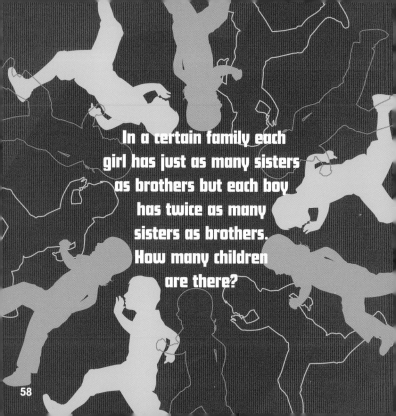

In a certain family each girl has just as many sisters as brothers but each boy has twice as many sisters as brothers. How many children are there?

58

Four buses leave the
garage at the same time on
the same day.
The first one returns to the
garage every 16 hours,
the second one every 12 hours,
the third one every 8 hours and
the fourth one every 4 hours.
How long will it be before they
all meet at the garage again?

A mystery number with two identical digits is multiplied by 99.
What is the four-digit number which results if its third digit is 3?

Mary was meant to proofread a document at the rate of 30 pages a day. Lazy Mary was halfway through the document before she realized that she was only working at the rate of 15 pages a day.

How fast does she need to proofread the rest of the document in order to reach her target of 30 pages a day?

A forgetful gran was searching for
presents for her two grandchildren.
However she couldn't remember
what sex they were, only that they
weren't both boys.
What is the probability
they are both girls?

Two horsemen started out
at daybreak.
They traveled the same
distance and arrived at their
destination at the same time.
Wyatt rode twice as long as
Billy rested and Billy rode
for three times as long as
Wyatt rested for.
Who rode the fastest?

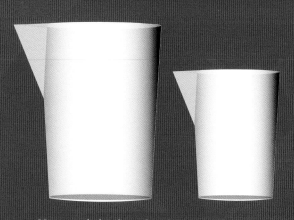

Mary needed 4 tbsp of vegetable stock for a recipe.
However, the only measuring containers she had
were 3 tbsp and 5 tbsp.
How can she measure out exactly 4 tbsp?

23				
				17

Fill in the magic square with the numbers 9 to 33 so that
all the columns, rows and diagonals add up to 105.

A six-digit number with 4 at the end becomes four times larger when the four is removed and put at the front.

What is the number?

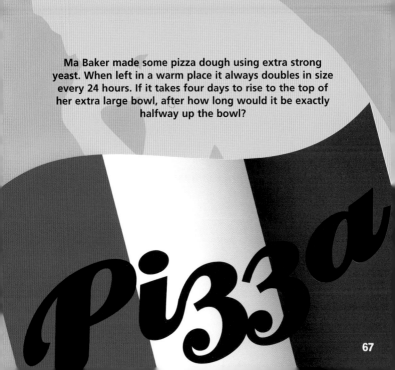

Ma Baker made some pizza dough using extra strong yeast. When left in a warm place it always doubles in size every 24 hours. If it takes four days to rise to the top of her extra large bowl, after how long would it be exactly halfway up the bowl?

Heather goes to a farm to buy eggs
but trips over and the farm stand
topples over with all the eggs.
Heather offers to pay for them.
The farmer can't remember how
many eggs there were but knows
that he could place two eggs in
each bag with one left over.
Same for three, four, five, and six eggs.
With seven, he's got none left.
How many eggs should Heather pay for?

An estate owner wants to landscape his garden so that every tree, bush and shrub is planted in groups of four. Each of these four must be the same distance from the other, once they're planted. How did he do it?

The Little Middleton Rotary Club has 500 members.
It organized a charity dinner where tickets were $14 for
new members and $20 for old members. All the new
members attended but only 70 percent of the old members
went. How much did the club make on ticket sales?

Ian buys a new car from a showroom 21 miles away from his house but drives his old car to go pick it up.

He has to get both his cars back home and devises a plan to do so.

He drives his old car 21 miles north to the showroom, parks it, picks up the new car and drives that one mile south.

He then locks it up, walks back north one mile to the dealer, picks up his old car drives it two miles.

He locks it up, walks back one mile, picks up the new car, drives it two miles south, locks it up, walks one mile back to the other car, and continues until he reaches home with both cars.

How many miles does he walk and drive in total?

A woman and her mother can reverse the digits in their ages.

They have been able to do that five times in the past and could do it twice more in the future.

How old is the woman now?

As he is driving, Glenn notices that the last four digits on
the odometer are a palindrome.
A mile later, the last five digits are also a palindrome.
Two miles later, all six are a palindrome.
What was the mileage when Glenn first looked at it?

Two brothers have a combined age of 42 years. Steve is twice as old as Bob was when Steve was as old as Bob is now. How old are they?

1058

A university creative writing course attracted 1058 students; half of those weren't very good and dropped out. The remainder were divided into an equal number of groups led by different tutors. Each of those groups had the same number of students. How many groups were there?

A man goes to a casino that requires a $1 entry and exit fee. The man plays the slots for three days, each day losing half his money, finally ending up broke. How much money did he start with?

In days of yore a prince was locked up in a tower with a jailer. The jailer took pity on the prince and said he would give him a chance to escape before they sent him to the gallows.

'I'm going to give you two boxes. One box has 50 white marbles, and one box has 50 black marbles. And I'm going to come in tomorrow morning and I'm going to pick a marble. I'll wear a blindfold so I can't see the marbles. And I'm going to pick a marble out. If it's white you escape and if it's black, you're a goner. You can do anything you want with the 100 marbles. There are 50 black ones and 50 white ones. You don't have to leave them in the two boxes as I have. You can put them all in one box. You can divide them up in any way between the two boxes. But you must use all the marbles.'

The prince's chances of dying have been reduced from 100% to 50% so he is a little cheered. He spends all night working out how to improve his chances even more and manages to improve his chance of escape to almost 75%. How?

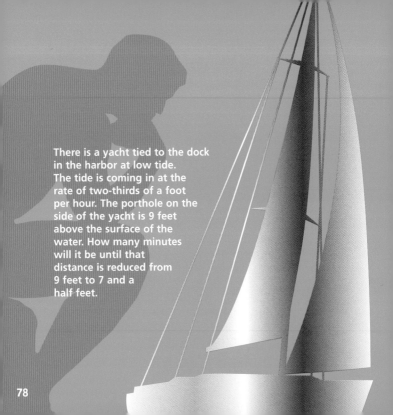

There is a yacht tied to the dock in the harbor at low tide. The tide is coming in at the rate of two-thirds of a foot per hour. The porthole on the side of the yacht is 9 feet above the surface of the water. How many minutes will it be until that distance is reduced from 9 feet to 7 and a half feet.

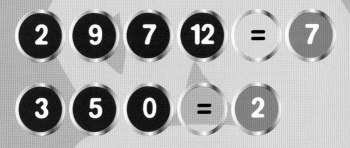

2 9 7 12 = 7

3 5 0 = 2

How would you write the number ten?

A struggling artist finds herself in difficult straights just after Christmas and realizes that she can't pay the rent for the month of January. So she approaches the landlord with the following proposition. She tells him

'I don't have any money to pay you the month of January's rent but I can give you a link of my gold necklace for every day that the rent is late.'

Her necklace has 31 links. The landlord verifies that it is 18-karat gold and agrees to the deal saying he'll return all the pieces at the end of the month. She could cut the necklace into 31 pieces and every day she would give him one piece, but then at the end of the month she would have to have the necklace repaired by a jeweler which would cost a lot. On day one she cuts off one link. On the second day she decides to cut off two and give him that pair of links, getting the first one back.

So how few cuts can she make in that month?

A woman has two children;
one's a boy.
What are the odds of
both being boys?

Princess Rowena fell in love with a knight, Rodney, and wanted to get married but her father, the Evil King Roland devised a way to drive off Rodney.
He put three boxes on the table. One was made of gold, one was silver, and the third was lead. Inside one of these boxes was a picture of Rowena. And Rodney was told to pick the one with Rowena's picture in it without opening the boxes and only then could he marry her.
On top of each box was an inscription.

The gold box said: Rowena's picture is in this box.
The silver box said: Rowena's picture is not in this box. The lead box said: Rowena's picture is not in the gold box.
Evil King Roland told Rodney that only one of the inscriptions is correct. So which box did Rodney choose in order to win Rowena's hand?

82

How do you make this equation equal 130?

(4) (7) (6) (4) (9) (7)
(3) (8) (5) (5) (6) (?)

What replaces the question mark?

At the local golf club lots of
balls have ended up in the lake.
If 100 balls have been lost in
the past five days with the
number increasing by six a day,
how many balls were lost five days ago?

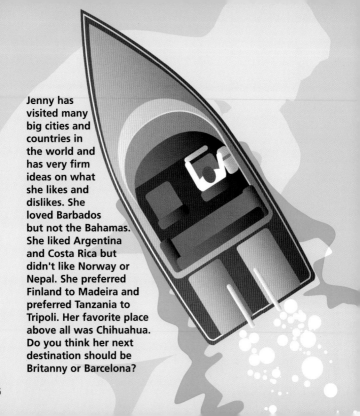

Jenny has visited many big cities and countries in the world and has very firm ideas on what she likes and dislikes. She loved Barbados but not the Bahamas. She liked Argentina and Costa Rica but didn't like Norway or Nepal. She preferred Finland to Madeira and preferred Tanzania to Tripoli. Her favorite place above all was Chihuahua. Do you think her next destination should be Britanny or Barcelona?

Page 6
49

Page 7
30 minutes. One assistant does two pairs of shoes and the other does three keys and one pair of shoes.

Page 8
$256

Page 9

9	11	18	5	22
3	25	7	14	16
12	19	1	23	10
21	8	15	17	4
20	2	24	6	13

Page 10
One solution is:
987654321 − 123456789
= 864197532

Page 11
1896 and 1903. 2,555 is an exact multiple of 365 so there are seven years intervening but not including a leap year. The two years must therefore be either side of 1900 which was not a leap year.

Page 12
12 + 3 − 4 + 5 − 6 = 10
2 + 2 − 3 + 4 − 5 = 0
7 − 6 + 2 + 5 − 1 = 7
5 + 4 − 3 − 1 + 4 = 9
8 − 4 + 5 − 2 + 1 = 8

Page 13
2 minutes 40 seconds

Page 14
N. If you start top left and move clockwise through alternate letters then letters advance by 2, then 3, then 4 etc.

Page 15

No. If the driver and hitcher were stationary then he would be correct but they are moving too. So the actual time between trucks is 20 minutes. So only three trucks enter the city every hour.

Page 16

Four seconds. If the time between the clapper striking the bell for the first peal and the second peal is two seconds then it will be a further two seconds before it strikes for a third peal.

Page 17

99. There was no year 0.

Page 18

Seven miles. It all depends on where on the globe he takes his walk. If he starts four miles from the South Pole and walks in a straight line towards it and then continues past it in a straight line he is now walking north and could continue a further three miles.

Page 19

Bill is 52, Ben is 39.

Page 20

443,546 – multiply the number by itself and subtract 10
1 – subtract 2 and divide by 2 alternately
79 – multiply by 2 and add 9 alternately
2 ie 1 1/1 25 – prime numbers with 2 added to each.

Page 21

$200

Page 22

Andrew receives 260, Bill 140 and Chris 70.

Page 23
1 in 24. There are 24 ways
1, 2, 3 and 4 can fall but only
1 is in ascending order.

Page 24

17	4	3	14
6	11	12	9
10	7	8	13
5	16	15	2

Page 25
$31. She has lost the $21 she
originally paid for the bracelet
and $10 she gave as change.
She failed to make the $4
profit but this cannot count
as money lost.

Page 26
$19,095.

Page 27
$21,474,836.47

Page 28
8:03

Page 29
Madge 30
Muriel 50
Mandy 40

Page 30
5 – the years of the two
World Wars
375 – 1,500 divided by
9, 8, 7 etc
27 – add 5 and subtract 2
alternately
536 – subtract 101 each
8,589,934,592 _ multiply each
number by half of itself

Page 31
$80

Page 32
Take $176 from Hank and $88
from Frank

Page 33
The teapot is $30.50 and the
strainer 50c.

Page 34
916 divided by 2 = 458
7 + 6 x 22 = 286

Page 35
True

Page 36
12
12
18
27
9
13

Page 37
7, 10 and 16

Page 38
There are a few equations but one is:
Aa + (a − a)(a + a + a...a)

Page 39
The faster clock gains on the slow one by the rate of one minute thirty seconds per hour. After 40 hours the faster clock will be exactly one hour ahead.

Page 40
A train traveling at 180 miles per hour takes 20 seconds to travel one mile and therefore 40 seconds to travel two miles plus 2 seconds for the complete train to pass any point making a total of 42 seconds.

Page 41
36

Page 42
27

Page 43
Possible solutions:
532 and 7641
632 and 8745
861, 932 and 745

Page 44
House numbers at 14 cents per digit

Page 45

After the first day

3	3	3
3	P	3
3	3	3

After the second day

4	1	4
1	P	1
4	1	4

Page 46

300

Page 47

Six squirrels would eat 100 acorns in 6,000 seconds

Page 48

They all have five letters in their name. No other number has that property.

Page 49

101

Page 50

11 + 1

Page 51

28

Page 52

Three

Page 53

The hands had actually swapped places. The meeting started at 10.59 and ended at 11.54.

Page 54

64.28 days

Page 55

Six

Page 56

Rob 8
Bob 12
Jim 5
Tim 20

Page 57

63 and 36

Page 58
Three boys and four girls

Page 59
48 hours

Page 60
6534 (99 x 66)

Page 61
She cannot do it since she has already used up all the time available completing just half the task.

Page 62
1 in 3

Page 63
Billy

Page 64
She should fill the 5 tbsp measurer and fill the 3 tbsp container with it. She should then tip the remaining 2 tbsp into the pan and repeat the process so she gets 4 tbsp.

Page 65

25	32	9	16	23
31	13	15	22	24
12	14	21	28	30
18	20	27	29	11
19	26	33	10	17

Page 66
102,564

Page 67
After three days

Page 68
301 eggs

Page 69
You'd plant the first three as an equilateral triangle, then you plant the fourth tree on the top of a hill which is precisely in the middle of the three, and at a height such that the size of the three new triangles that you make are the same as the original triangle that was made by the first three that were planted.

Page 70
$7,000

Page 71
84 miles

Page 72
57

Page 73
198888 then it was
1988889 followed by
19888891

Page 74
Bob is 18, Steve 24.

Page 75
23

Page 76
$21

Page 77
He puts 99 marbles in one box, and one white marble in the other box. The jailer has a 50-50 chance of picking a box. So if he picks the one with the white marble in it, then the prince is automatically going to improve his chances to 100%. If he picks the other box, then his chances are still almost 50%. So overall his chances of surviving are almost 75%.

Page 78
If the boat is floating, it will continue to float and the porthole will be raised up as the boat is raised up and the distance will be the same.

Page 79
3, 9, 12.

Page 80
Five.

Page 81
One in three

Page 82

The silver box. If only one of them is true the inscription on the gold box cannot be true, because if it is, then the inscription on the silver box must also be true. So, the statement on the lead box is the only one that can be true.

Page 83

Page 84

10. Add two top numbers and subtract bottom left.

Page 85

8

Page 86

Britanny. She loves repeated consonants.

Other titles in the Mindbending range include:

Mindbending Conundrums

Mindbending Lateral Thinking

Mindbending Speed Puzzles

LAGOON
BOOKS